Mature Reading Instru

King Lear
Part 1

B
Piper
Books

INSTRUCTION

The only prompting required is 'Say the sounds and read the word'. When help is needed, do nothing more than say: 'The sound here is ____'

Insist on accurate reading at all times: each person differs but each must learn to handle the same Alphabetic Code.

Don't allow guessing – it is a very difficult habit to eradicate.

Avoid explanations, hints, and other 'help'.

Ensure that attention is paid to 'reading through the word' – in particular with word endings.

Encourage rereading of earlier books. This will increase confidence.

Use the stories to develop vocabulary and communication after the reading.

King Lear

CAST:

LEAR, the old King, about to give up his crown to his girls:

GONERIL, his first-born

REGAN, his second-born

CORDELIA, his third-born

DUKE OF ALBANY, husband to GONERIL

DUKE OF CORNWALL, husband to REGAN

KING OF FRANCE, wishes to wed CORDELIA

EARL OF KENT, LEAR's best chum

EARL OF GLOS, well-meaning lord. His sons:

EDGAR, his first-born

EDMUND, his bastard child

JESTER, LEAR's clown

First Act: Sharper than Serpents' Teeth

At King Lear's palace:

Lear: I am heading for my grave! And I wish to shake all cares from my elderly bones. So I am laying down my crown and dividing my kingdom between my three lucky girls! Speak up… who loves daddy best?

Goneril: Me, me!

Regan: No, me! With all my heart!

Goneril: More than freedom itself; beyond all that's rich and rare; no less than life itself; as much as child ever loved –

Regan: Yes, all that! But even more so! NOTHING makes me happy but my dad!

Cordelia: Don't you both have husbands?

GONERIL and REGAN [*shrugging*]: Yes, what about them?

LEAR: My dear dear girls! Here, have a third of my kingdom each! Now, Cordelia my sweet… what can YOU say to win even more lands than Goneril and Regan?

CORDELIA: Nothing.

LEAR [*scowling*]: Nothing will come of nothing: speak up!

CORDELIA: Unhappy as I am, I cannot heave my heart into my mouth. I'm fond of you, but you can't have all my love, I'm saving much of it for when I get wed.

LEAR: Better you had not been born than not to have pleased me better. OUT!

EARL OF KENT: My King! Check this evil rashness!

LEAR: Come not between the dragon and his fury! I loved her best! And she kicked me in the teeth! She's no lass of mine! OUT! BOTH of you!

KENT: Lear, *please*. We've been chums for years. I don't want to abandon you with those heartless girls, just when you're getting old –

LEAR: Out! NOW! Or – chop, chop – head on the block! Okay, you – French King! You still want to marry this wench, now she has nothing but my hate? She had the CHEEK to say she'd love her husband as much as me!

KING OF FRANCE: I think I can live with that. Yes, I'll snatch up what's cast away! Come, Cordelia, Queen of France!

LEAR: Goneril – Regan – now you'll get FIFTY per cent of my kingdom each! And I'll take it in turns to stay with each of you – just me and the hundred men I'm going to keep for myself!

GONERIL and REGAN: Lovely, daddy! [*Hushed*] Gods, how senile *is* he?

AT THE EARL OF GLOS'S PALACE:

EDMUND: My dad is the Earl of Glos himself! Yet I am *nothing*! Branded as 'base' – just cos mum wasn't wed to dad! Am I not as fine, as well-made, as my brother Edgar? What's so great about dull, stale wedlock? Now gods, stand up for bastards! Aaaah! I mean hello, dad!

EARL OF GLOS: What's that letter you're hiding?

EDMUND: Letter, what letter... oh heck! You got me. Okay, it's from my big brother Edgar... I'm hoping it's all a big joke.

GLOS: Why?

EDMUND: Cos it recommends that we kill you off and divide the earldom between us.

GLOS: It WHAT! He cannot be such a monster! To his father, who so tenderly loves him!

EDMUND: Quite! Tell you what, I'll have a chat with him... see what's going on... [*yells*] Hey, Edgar! Dad's taken a dislike to you all of a sudden! I'd get out of here if I were you... quickly!

EDGAR [*entering*]: But why! What have I *done*...? Some evil-doer must be lying about me!

EDMUND [*tut-tuts sadly*]: That is indeed my fear. Quick, I hear dad! Flee while you still can! He wants you arrested, so I must pretend to wave my dagger at you... you do the same to me... and *flee*! *Now*!

EDGAR flees. EDMUND cuts himself with his dagger.

EDMUND: Daddy! Did you SEE that? Edgar wanted to KILL me! My dear brother!

GLOS: He's no son of mine! I'll kill him! All my lands will go to you! Oh, my old heart is cracked, it's cracked!

EDMUND [*to himself*]: Tee hee! My witless kin trust me so much! Let me, if not by birth, inherit lands by my wits!

* * * * *

AT THE PALACE OF GONERIL'S HUSBAND, THE DUKE OF ALBANY:

GONERIL: Each day that maddening old man upsets me more! I'll not put up with it! It's nag, nag, nag from him, and nothing but stress from the hundred men he's inflicted on us! Which bit of 'I'm giving up my powers' did he somehow not understand? Let's try neglecting him! If he dislikes it, let him storm off to my sister, whose mind is the same as mine on this matter!

The exiled EARL OF KENT enters, in a fake beard.

KENT: Now, banished Kent, if nobody spots that
the bearded bloke is you, you can help Lear... who
you love however senile he's become. Oh, hello, my
King! I'm here to serve you!

LEAR: You are? That's nice. I have felt a neglect
of late, a lack of kindness. I dismissed it as a silly
fancy, but we'll see... Ah, here's my jester!

JESTER: Ah, here's the moron who gave away his
crown and all his lands! Nothing will come of nothing; remind me what you have now...

LEAR: Have a care, you lying scoundrel! I'll have
you whipped!

JESTER: I marvel that you, Goneril and Regan
are related; they'll have me whipped for telling
the truth, you'll have me whipped for lying. And
sometimes I am whipped for holding my peace.

GONERIL enters, frowning.

LEAR: My lass! How come you frown so?

JESTER: How happy the days when you didn't have to care if she was frowning!

GONERIL [*glaring*]: This jester – and all the other men you've inflicted on me – are nothing but pests. Don't think I'll let them get away with it! Start sacking them – NOW!

LEAR: Are – you – my – child? I cannot be awake... I cannot be Lear... Who'd speak so to the King? Who am I? Who told me I had children? You, girl! What name shall I call you by?

GONERIL: Oh, these silly jokes... exactly what has to stop! You are old; so be wise. That escort brings nothing but greed, lust, and anger. So just sack... say... fifty of them.

LEAR: Darkness and devils! Call my men together; get my horses! I'll not stay to vex you! I have still a lass to welcome me! Oh hard-hearted offspring! Oh Lear, Lear, Lear! [*Strikes his head*] Beat at this gate, that let such folly in! Oh you gods – if Goneril breeds, let it be a torment to her! So that she feels how sharper than serpent's teeth it is to have a thankless child! Oh, let me not be mad, not mad! Sweet heaven, keep me in temper; I'd not be mad!

LEAR reaches the EARL OF GLOS's palace, where REGAN and her husband the DUKE OF CORNWALL are staying:

LEAR: Will not speak with me? They are sick? They are weary? No they are NOT!

GLOS: I am so sorry, my lord. I wish all was well between you, but…

LEAR: The King will speak with the Duke of Cornwall and his wife! I – will – speak – to – my – girl! NOW!

REGAN [*enters, gritting her teeth*]: Hello dad, I'm glad to see you.

LEAR: I HOPE you're glad to see me... if not, you are no lass of mine.

REGAN: Charming.

LEAR: Oh Regan, Goneril is nothing; she has treated me with such sharp-fanged unkindness –

REGAN: Surely not – it's much more likely that *you* have mistreated *her*! I keep getting letters from her about those hundred men you insist on keeping. Why don't you just beg her forgiveness?

LEAR: Over – my – dead – body!

REGAN: Oh, I think I can hear Goneril coming now; do bear in mind you're old and weak, and start acting like it! Sack fifty of those men and return home with her!

LEAR: Return with *her* and but fifty men? I'd rather
live outside as comrade to the wolf and the owl;
I'd rather grovel to that French King who wed
Cordelia; I'd rather be a slave!

GONERIL [*entering*]: Fine by me. Hello daddy!

LEAR: I beg you, do not make me mad; I'll not
pester you. Farewell, my child; we'll no more meet.
I'll not call on the gods to strike you down; I'll just
stay with Regan, I and my hundred men.

REGAN: Ah... um... well... I'm not really ready
for you yet... if you DO stay with me, I can't cope
with more than twenty-five men.

LEAR: I gave you all —

REGAN: You made us hang around for a heck of a
long time first.

LEAR: Fine! I'll go with Goneril! She offers me fifty men; you offer me twenty-five; she loves me TWICE as much as you do!

GONERIL: Think about it! I have plenty of servants to tend to you – what need you of twenty-five, ten, or even *five* men?

REGAN: Five? Hell's bells, what need have you of even a lone man?

LEAR: Oh, stop! The basest beggar has something more than he needs! Oh heavens – you see me here, a luckless old man, so full of distress! If it is you gods who stir these girls' hearts to hate me, at least do not let me bear it tamely! YOU VILE HAGS! I will have such repayment on you that all the lands shall – I will do such things – what they are I cannot yet think, but they shall be TERRORS! You think I'll weep; no, I'll not weep. Storm and tempest! I have reason to weep, but this heart shall break into a hundred fragments before I'll weep!

LEAR storms out into the storm.

— End of First Act —